D1459260

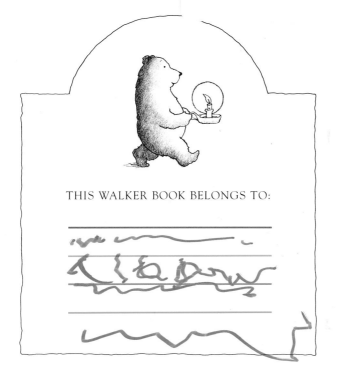

THIS WALKER BOOK BELONGS TO:

red nose readers

So Can I

Allan Ahlberg

Colin McNaughton

Rob a Rabbit
Push and Pull
So Can I

WALKER BOOKS
AND SUBSIDIARIES
LONDON • BOSTON • SYDNEY

First published 1985 by
Walker Books Ltd
87 Vauxhall Walk
London SE11 5HJ

This edition published 1987
Reprinted 1989, 1993, 1995, 1997, 1999, 2005

Text © 1985 Allan Ahlberg
Illustrations © 1985 Colin McNaughton

Printed in China

British Library Cataloguing in Publication Data
A catalogue record for this book is
available from the British Library.

ISBN 0-7445-1016-3

www.walkerbooks.co.uk

Rob a Rabbit

rob a rabbit

rob a baby

rob a king

rob a pirate

rob a Santa

rob a ...

. . .robber

Push and Pull

pull

and
push

push

and pull

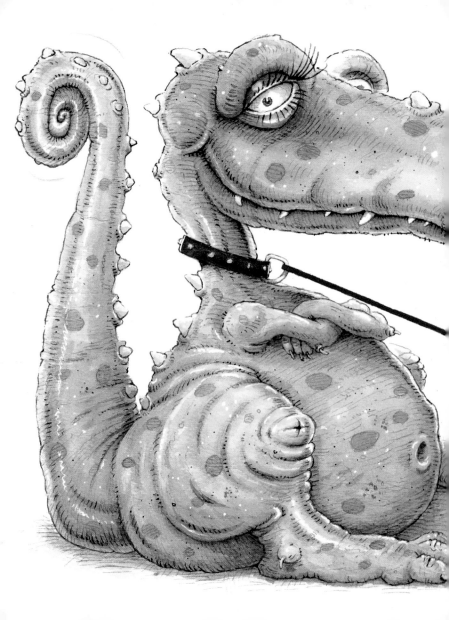

pull

and push

So Can I

I can
clean my teeth.

I can
write my name.

I can
read a book.

So can I!

I can
carry the shopping.

I can
clean my teeth
and
write my name
and
read a book
and
carry the shopping.

the end

red nose readers

RED NOSE READERS

Allan Ahlberg / Colin McNaughton

Red Nose Readers are the easiest of easy readers – and the funniest!
Red for single words and phrases. Yellow for simple sentences.
Blue for memorable rhymes. How many have you got?

RED BOOKS

Bear's Birthday • Big Bad Pig • Fee Fi Fo Fum
Happy Worm • Help! • Jumping
Make a Face • So Can I

YELLOW BOOKS

Crash! Bang! Wallop! • Push the Dog
Me and My Friend • Shirley's Shops

BLUE BOOKS

Look Out for the Seals! • One, Two, Flea!
Tell Us A Story • Blow Me Down!

FOR THE BEST CHILDREN'S BOOKS,
LOOK FOR THE BEAR

www.walkerbooks.co.uk